Book **D**

Specific Skill Series

Drawing Conclusions

Richard A. Boning

Fifth Edition

D1304078

SRA/McGraw-Hill
Columbus, Ohio

Cover, Back Cover, James D. Watt/Masterfile

SRA/McGraw-Hill

A Division of The McGraw·Hill Companies

Send all inquiries to:
    SRA/McGraw-Hill
    8787 Orion Place
    Columbus, OH 43240-4027

ISBN 0-02-687984-0

    8 9 IPC 02 01

PURPOSE:

DRAWING CONCLUSIONS helps develop one of the most important interpretive skills. Pupils learn to look beyond the writer's literal statements to reach an unstated but logical conclusion based on those statements and sometimes their phrasing. In DRAWING CONCLUSIONS the correct conclusion is the most logical one for pupils to reach from only the information presented.

FOR WHOM:

The skill of DRAWING CONCLUSIONS is developed through a series of books spanning ten levels (Picture, Preparatory, A, B, C, D, E, F, G, H). The Picture Level is for pupils who have not acquired a basic sight vocabulary. The Preparatory Level is for pupils who have a basic sight vocabulary but are not yet ready for the first-grade-level book. Books A through H are appropriate for pupils who can read on levels one through eight, respectively. **The use of the *Specific Skill Series Placement Test* is recommended to determine the appropriate level.**

THE NEW EDITION:

The fifth edition of the *Specific Skill Series* maintains the quality and focus that has distinguished this program for more than 25 years. A key element central to the program's success has been the unique nature of the reading selections. Nonfiction pieces about current topics have been designed to stimulate the interest of students, motivating them to use the comprehension strategies they have learned to further their reading. To keep this important aspect of the program intact, a percentage of the reading selections have been replaced in order to ensure the continued relevance of the subject material.

In addition, a significant percentage of the artwork in the program has been replaced to give the books a contemporary look. The cover photographs are designed to appeal to readers of all ages.

SESSIONS:

Short practice sessions are the most effective. It is desirable to have a practice session every day or every other day, using a few units each session.

To the Teacher

SCORING:

Pupils should record their answers on the reproducible worksheets. The worksheets make scoring easier and provide uniform records of the pupils' work. Using worksheets also avoids consuming the exercise books.

It is important for pupils to know how well they are doing. For this reason, units should be scored as soon as they have been completed. Then a discussion can be held in which pupils justify their choices. (The Integrated Language Activities, many of which are open-ended, do not lend themselves to an objective score; thus there are no answer keys for these pages.)

GENERAL INFORMATION ON *DRAWING CONCLUSIONS*:

The questions in DRAWING CONCLUSIONS do not deal with direct references; thus the answers do not use the same words as the paragraphs. On the Picture Level, the readers examine the picture for the correct answer. The Preparatory, A, and B levels contain primarily indirect references; that is, the answers are found in the paragraphs but with slightly different wording. Some easy conclusions are also included. As the books advance in challenge, there are more difficult conclusions, involving less obvious relationships. The conclusions also become more dependent on qualifying words such as "mostly," "all," "some," or "only."

In DRAWING CONCLUSIONS the readers are asked to find an example, note a contrast, generalize, see cause and effect relationships, detect a mood, see an analogy, identify a time or place relationship, make a comparison, or anticipate an outcome.

It is important that the teacher ask pupils to find in the paragraph the specific information relevant to the tentative conclusion. Then pupils must test the conclusion against the information provided. When the emphasis is placed on finding evidence to prove answers and when the pupils put themselves in roles of detectives, not only does their ability to draw conclusions rapidly improve, but they also have fun.

Pupils must know that a conclusion is a judgment made. It must be supported by strong evidence. In DRAWING CONCLUSIONS the correct answer is one that is either highly likely or certain.

Some alternate answer choices may be true. The answer that is accepted as correct, however, must not only be true but must have supportive evidence in the paragraph. The clue may hinge on a single word, involve a phrase or a sentence, or encompass the paragraph as a whole.

RELATED MATERIALS:

Specific Skill Series Placement Tests, which enable the teacher to place pupils at their appropriate levels in each skill, are available for the Elementary (Pre-1–6) and Midway (4–8) grade levels.

About This Book

When you read, you can often figure out things that the writer doesn't tell you directly. You do this by thinking about the information the author does tell you. When you figure out something the author does not state directly, you are **drawing conclusions**.

Good readers draw conclusions as they read. They use the information the writer gives them to figure out things that the writer does not say. Read this paragraph. What conclusion can you draw about when Hawaii became a state?

> Hawaii and Alaska, which became states in the same year, are very different from each other. Alaska became the largest state when it joined the Union on January 3, 1959. Hawaii, the last state to join the Union, is one of the nation's smallest states.

Did you figure out that Hawaii became a state after January 3, 1959, but before January 1, 1960? You can draw this conclusion from the information the writer gives.

In this book, you will read paragraphs. After you read each paragraph, draw a conclusion about something in the paragraph. Use the information in the paragraph to figure out the correct answer.

1.   The saying "You don't know your own strength" must be true. Mildred Ludwick of Hawaii saw a little girl get struck by a car. The girl became pinned under a wheel. Ludwick used all her might and lifted the three-thousand-pound car off the girl. Ludwick weighed only 105 pounds.

2.   Before the 1800s, people didn't have right or left shoes. They had shoes of just one shape that they used for both feet. When people first saw right and left shoes, they laughed. They called them "crooked shoes." "What a silly idea!" they said.

3.   Hippopotamuses in zoos eat anything. In the stomach of a dead hippo were a .25-caliber bullet, valve caps, $2.50 in coins, rocks and stones, transportation tokens, nuts, bolts, screws, wire, a pocketbook, and a lipstick, among other things. The hippo had died (of a foot infection) after forty-five years in the Washington Zoo.

4.   Some plants eat meat in addition to making their own food. The Venus flytrap, as you might guess, eats flies. Other plants send out the smell of food. Then they catch the insects that come close to see what the smell is.

5.   Alaskan huskies wear booties as they race over the frozen snow! These dogs, which pull the drivers and the long, narrow sleds, weigh as much as fifty pounds. The huskies need five thousand calories plus three to four quarts of liquid a day. They run at speeds of nine to twelve miles per hour.

1. A good nickname for Mildred Ludwick might be—

   (A) **Merry Mildred**

   (B) **Lucky Ludwick**

   (C) **Mighty Mildred**

---

2. You can tell that shoes before 1800—

   (A) **were pretty**

   (B) **didn't fit very well**

   (C) **didn't look alike**

---

3. You can tell that—

   (A) **there are many hippos in Washington**

   (B) **most hippos live forty-five years**

   (C) **people throw things into zoo cages**

---

4. The paragraph suggests that—

   (A) **Venus flytraps can move**

   (B) **all plants smell like food**

   (C) **meat-eating plants mostly eat insects**

---

5. You can tell that Alaskan huskies, like people,—

   (A) **need the proper food and clothing**

   (B) **live in houses made of ice**

   (C) **enjoy the beautiful sights of Alaska**

1.   In the Inland Sea of Japan, there are apartment houses for eels and octopuses. Rows of hollow concrete blocks with windowlike openings on all sides were built on the ocean floor. The blocks slow the current along the bottom and make better feeding and breeding grounds for the fish.

2.   Young men of the eighteenth century favored bear grease to groom their hair. Barbers were anxious to prove that the bear grease they sold was genuine. Some barbers went so far as to place a live bear in a cage outside their shops!

3.   When people go to sleep, they do not remain in the same position. Most people move thirty-five or forty times during the course of the night. They shift constantly from one side to the other and from their backs to their stomachs.

4.   The largest flying bird is the albatross. This giant bird has a wingspread of twelve feet, tip to tip. The body of the bird weighs about sixteen pounds and is nearly four feet long. The albatross is found in the South Pacific and the South Atlantic ocean areas.

5.   Whales and elephants take up a lot of room. So do the billions of people on Earth. But ninety percent of the living material on the planet comes from plants—trees, moss, grass, and the like.

UNIT 2

1. In a fast current, it is hard for fish to—

    (A) swim

    (B) see

    (C) eat

2. You can tell that young men in the eighteenth century—

    (A) cared little about their appearance

    (B) did not make their own hairdressing

    (C) wore their hair short

3. From the story you can't tell—

    (A) why people move in their sleep

    (B) how many times people move in their sleep

    (C) the positions people sleep in

4. You would most likely see an albatross—

    (A) at the North Pole

    (B) off South America

    (C) in a pet shop

5. The paragraph suggests that—

    (A) trees weigh more than whales

    (B) plants take up more room than animals

    (C) there are more people than elephants

1.   Softball was first played in the late 1800s—indoors! The bases were closer together than baseball bases. A large "soft ball" was created and bats smaller than baseball bats were put into use. The pitching style was changed to an underhand pitch for softball, instead of the overhead throw used for baseball.

2.   Our fingernails and toenails aren't of much help. We can use our fingernails to scratch with. Maybe they give a little support to the tips of our fingers. Our toenails don't seem to have any useful purpose. It seems strange that we have them.

3.   There is a flower called "Farewell to Spring." It grows in the Northwest of our country. "Farewell," of course, means "good-by." This flower begins to bloom when spring comes to an end. It stays in bloom through the summer, until October.

4.   In the Middle Ages beds were rare. Often an entire household had only one. When a wealthy person went visiting, the bed was taken along. It was carried in a special wagon. An entire group of servants, who were trained to put it together and take it down, went with it.

5.   When a bird lands, it has to be careful that it doesn't tumble forward. Like an airplane, the bird lands into the wind. The wind acts as a brake. Some birds fan the tail and turn it downward. The legs absorb much of the shock.

1. You can tell that softball—

    (A) is easier to play than baseball

    (B) was copied from baseball

    (C) is played indoors today

---

2. Fingernails can be used for—

    (A) one purpose

    (B) two purposes

    (C) no purpose

---

3. Another good name for the plant could be—

    (A) "Farewell to Winter"

    (B) "Hello to Summer"

    (C) "Good-by to Everybody"

---

4. You can tell that beds were—

    (A) comfortable

    (B) used only by royal families

    (C) sometimes carried in sections

---

5. Birds that land in the same direction as the wind are likely to—

    (A) fall sideways

    (B) overshoot the landing spot

    (C) undershoot the landing spot

1.   An octopus can change colors. Usually the octopus takes the color of its surroundings. This is not so when it becomes upset. It may get pale all over or turn brown or even purple. The octopus keeps on changing colors, one after another, until it settles down.

2.   Babies have to learn to see. Newborn babies can't see shapes clearly. They can tell the difference between very bright things and dark things, but they can't follow things. It takes them a few weeks to see shapes and a few months to see colors.

3.   Horses are measured in units called *hands*. A hand is four inches, or about the width of a person's palm. The measurement is taken from the ground to the highest point of the withers, which are where the neck joins the back.

4.   The chameleon has the most unusual tongue of any creature. A fly would seem to be safe thirteen inches away from an eight-inch chameleon. But the chameleon opens its mouth, and its long pink tongue flashes out. In a twinkling the fly has been swallowed!

5.   A strange ship, named the *Fram*, can be seen in Oslo, Norway. It was built for exploring the Arctic Ocean in the late 1800s. Because of its shape and strong frame, it was never crushed by moving ice from glaciers. As ice pinched against it, the *Fram* was lifted up to glide over and along with the moving ice.

1. When an octopus is the color of the surroundings, it is—

    (A) happy
    (B) upset
    (C) dead

2. By using their eyes, newborn babies can tell—

    (A) an orange from an apple
    (B) a pencil from a pen
    (C) night from day

3. A horse is measured from the—

    (A) ground to the top of the head
    (B) top of the saddle to the ground
    (C) ground to the bottom of the neck

4. You can tell that the fly—

    (A) doesn't know about the chameleon's tongue
    (B) thinks it's stronger than the chameleon
    (C) is very brave to approach the chameleon

5. The *Fram* became famous because it—

    (A) hit an iceberg
    (B) sailed on ice
    (C) broke speed records

1.   Once, the kind of bread people ate depended on how rich they were. Rich people ate white bread. It was white because the bran, or outer shell of the seed, had been removed from the flour. Today people know that whole-bran bread, once eaten by the poor, is richest in food value.

---

2.   The earliest-blooming wildflower in the North blooms before the snow is off the ground. In February it is possible to scrape away the snow and uncover skunk cabbage. As one might suspect, skunk cabbage doesn't have a pleasant smell.

---

3.   If you have a nosebleed, it is best to lie on your back. Try pinching your nostrils for about five minutes. Placing a cold, damp towel on the neck sometimes helps stop the nosebleed. Try to stay calm. Most nosebleeds stop after a few minutes.

---

4.   Some people think that snakes have to be coiled before they can strike. Don't believe it. It isn't necessary for a snake to coil its body in order to strike. The snake won't take the time to arrange itself if it sees an enemy close by.

---

5.   Racehorses can't be given just any name. There is a rule that horses' names can't cover more than sixteen spaces—and that includes both the letters and the spaces between the words. Racehorses are also not allowed to take the name of another horse.

1. You can tell that—

    (A) **bran is healthful**

    (B) **white bread is easier to slice**

    (C) **bran is bitter and hard**

2. You can tell that most wildflowers in the North—

    (A) **bloom only in the snow**

    (B) **bloom all year long**

    (C) **don't bloom before February**

3. To stop a nosebleed—

    (A) **is very difficult**

    (B) **position counts**

    (C) **temperature doesn't count**

4. You are safe from the snake if—

    (A) **it is not coiled**

    (B) **you are far away**

    (C) **it is coiled**

5. A good name for a racehorse might be—

    (A) **Captain Lightning**

    (B) **Run Fast**

    (C) **Super Saddle Speeder**

1. Crisfield, Maryland, is a pretty crabby place. This town on Chesapeake Bay is one of America's chief crab-fishing centers. So each year the people there have a "Crab Festival," with a crab parade, crab races, a crab-picking contest, and so on.

---

2. Have you been to a piñata party? If so, you know about the goodies inside the piñata, which is a hollow clay or paper figure, often in the shape of an animal. The piñata hangs from the ceiling by a string. Blindfolded party-goers strike at the piñata with a stick. When the piñata is broken, and the treasures fall out, all scramble to get their fair share.

---

3. Most parents like to keep their babies clean. This is not the case with a mother rhinoceros. Just as soon as her baby is born, she gives it a mud bath. The mud protects the hide of the young rhino from the sun.

---

4. If you live in the city of Birmingham, Houston, or Baton Rouge, you are sinking. These cities and others are taking too much of their drinking water out of the ground. As water is removed, the earth settles lower into the empty underground space. Houston is already five feet lower than it was sixty-five years ago.

---

5. Can you imagine building a ship that can't sink? The Japanese believe that they have such a ship. Each of the four middle parts is filled with plastic foam rather than air. This hard, light, plastic foam keeps water from getting into each section.

1. You can tell that—

    (A) no one likes the "Crab Festival"

    (B) Crisfield's people like to have fun

    (C) Crisfield's people are not nice

---

2. Party-goers must destroy the piñata before they get—

    (A) chances to pin the tail on the piñata

    (B) what is stored inside it

    (C) sticks to strike at the piñata

---

3. You can tell that—

    (A) a mother rhinoceros is naturally untidy

    (B) a mother rhinoceros cares little for her baby

    (C) the skin of a young rhinoceros is tender

---

4. These cities are sinking—

    (A) so fast that there is great danger

    (B) so slowly that there is little danger

    (C) because they get too much rain

---

5. In the whole ship there are—

    (A) four parts

    (B) more than four parts

    (C) two parts

A. Exercising Your Skill

Do you enjoy riddles? Did you ever stop to think that when you solve a riddle, you are really **drawing a conclusion**? A conclusion is a guess you make. The guess is based on facts. Read the riddles below and think about the facts each one gives. Write the answers to each riddle on your paper.

1. What walks around all day and sits under the bed at night with its tongue hanging out?
2. How can you make a sling sing?
3. Why is it that you find what you are looking for in the last place you look?
4. What kind of keys can't open locks?
5. What word is always pronounced wrong?
6. When the clock strikes thirteen, what time is it?
7. What looks like a cat, eats like a cat, acts like a cat, but is not a cat?
8. The more you take away, the bigger it gets. What is it?
9. How many months have 28 days?
10. What stays hot no matter how cold it gets?

B. Expanding Your Skill

Take turns asking and answering the riddles. Did everyone come up with the same answers? Why or why not? Talk with your classmates about the facts you used to solve the riddles. Then turn this page upside down to check the answers to the riddles.

Answers: 1. a shoe, a sneaker; 2. take away the letter l; 3. because you hadn't yet found what you were looking for; 4. monkeys, donkeys; turkeys; 5. wrong; 6. time to get the clock fixed; 7. a kitten; 8. a hole; 9. all of them; 10. pepper.

C. Exploring Language

What makes a joke funny? In order to understand a joke, you need to draw a conclusion about the facts. Read each of the jokes below. On your paper, answer the questions about the jokes.

1. One fisher asked another, "Is this a good lake for fish?" The second fisher answered, "It must be. I can't get any of them to come out."

   What problem was the second fisher having? Tell the class.

2. A woman called up the radio station and asked to speak to the person who reported the weather. She told her, "I thought you'd be interested to know that I shoveled two feet of 'partly cloudy' from my front steps this morning!"

   What had the weather reporter said the weather would be like? What was it really like? Tell the class.

3. Jim Joker's grandfather said, "When I was your age, Jim Joker, I could name all the presidents." "I know, Grandpa," said Jim Joker, "but there were only three or four of them then!"

   What was Jim Joker saying about his grandfather? Tell the class.

D. Expressing Yourself

Choose one of these activities.

1. Create your own riddles to ask your classmates. See whether they can guess the answers to your riddles by using the facts you give.

2. With a group of classmates, plan and put on a comedy show. Each person should memorize two or three jokes for the show.

1.   During colonial days there were no bathtubs or showers in the houses. They were not missed, however. Many people of that time never thought of taking a bath. Most people thought that water caused many diseases. Only the hands and face were washed, and that wasn't often.

2.   Usually the bones of birds' wings are hollow. This gives the bones strength without weight. The surface of the wing is curved. The fact that the front edge of the wing is thicker than the rear edge also makes for easier flight.

3.   Sometimes we see sand dunes near the water. These sand dunes do not always stay in the same place. The wind blows them along. Some sand dunes move only a few feet each year. Others move over two hundred feet in a year.

4.   Between 1840 and 1890, thousands of Americans went west. Most of these pioneers went in wagon trains (a number of covered wagons traveling together). At Independence, Missouri, the wagon trains gathered. From there two main pathways branched out—the California and Oregon trails to the north and the Santa Fe Trail to the south.

5.   The Gulf Stream is made up of a flow of warm ocean water a thousand times as great as the flow of the Amazon River. Scientists have mapped the Gulf Stream's course up the Atlantic Coast. When it heads toward Europe, it disappears. Where? No one knows.

1. You can tell that people of today—

   (A) take more baths than people of colonial days

   (B) take fewer baths than people of colonial days

   (C) fear water more than people of colonial days

2. If the *back* edge of its wing were thick too, a bird—

   (A) could fly better

   (B) would fly upside down

   (C) couldn't fly as well

3. Sand dunes move the most—

   (A) where it is coldest

   (B) where it is windiest

   (C) near the water

4. You can tell that Independence, Missouri, was once—

   (A) an important railroad station

   (B) the starting point for people going farther west

   (C) the capital of the state of Missouri

5. We know that the Gulf Stream—

   (A) is full of icebergs

   (B) affects the Atlantic Coast

   (C) is located in England

1.   Life was not easy for the pioneer women. They often worked beside their husbands in the fields, made their own soap and candles, and spun and wove their own cloth. They also cared for their children and cooked for everyone. These women helped create a home for their families in the wilderness.

---

2.   If there were no air or dust, we would see the stars both day and night. The sky wouldn't be blue. It would look jet black. With no dust or air, there wouldn't be any twilight. When the sun went down, we would have total darkness at once.

---

3.   Some animals are more comfortable if they sleep standing up. When the African elephant lies down, its great weight presses on its lungs. It is difficult for the animal to breathe. It usually chooses to sleep while standing. Standing or lying down, a sleeping African elephant snores loudly!

---

4.   Some people who live very close to nature have very highly developed senses and powers of endurance that science finds hard to understand. The Bush People of Africa can run along the desert at seven miles an hour for five hours. They are able to hear an aircraft landing forty-five miles away!

---

5.   A new door latch opens only if the right person presses the button. The caller's fingerprints are checked against the fingerprints of the people who live in the house. These are stored in a tiny computer inside the lock. If the fingerprints match, the latch opens.

1. You can tell that pioneer women—

    (A) led busy and useful lives

    (B) did no heavy work

    (C) had good educations

2. Air and dust help us to see—

    (A) darkness

    (B) color

    (C) distance

3. African elephants—

    (A) always sleep lying down

    (B) sometimes sleep while standing

    (C) always sleep standing up

4. People close to nature may be superior in—

    (A) three ways

    (B) four ways

    (C) two ways

5. The new lock makes it very difficult—

    (A) for everyone to enter

    (B) for burglars to enter

    (C) to keep people out

1. In Tennessee lies a large beautiful lake—inside a giant cave. It is the world's largest underground lake. Years ago people named it the "Lost Sea." In the 1800s Indians or Southern soldiers would hide in the cave, by the lake. The cave with the Lost Sea was once even used as a dance hall.

---

2. Cats have a good ear for music! More than one musician has depended upon a cat to pick out a note that was slightly off-key. Cats can tell the difference between two notes that are even closer than the distance between notes heard in songs.

---

3. Can you picture a coin so big that you can hardly carry it? The country of Sweden had such a coin over two hundred years ago. It was two feet long and one foot wide. The coin weighed thirty-one pounds.

---

4. Rain is the biggest danger to baby birds. During rainy weather, the parents have to leave the nest in search of food. The baby birds are left uncovered. The babies get chilled. Thousands have been known to die during long rainstorms.

---

5. In the year 1100, Mrs. Silvie of Venice, Italy, tried to introduce forks to tableware because she didn't like eating meat with her hands. People thought of her as odd. Most people didn't start using forks until about four hundred years later.

1. A name you would *not* give the Lost Sea is—

   (A) "Sunny Lake"

   (B) "Hidden Lake"

   (C) "Dark Lake"

2. You can tell that—

   (A) cats are music lovers

   (B) cats can help tune pianos

   (C) musicians dislike cats

3. One of these coins couldn't fit in your—

   (A) closet

   (B) pocket

   (C) room

4. Most of the time baby birds are covered mainly by—

   (A) the trees

   (B) the nest

   (C) their mothers and fathers

5. Most people began using forks—

   (A) when they watched Mrs. Silvie

   (B) before 1100

   (C) in the 1500s

1.   Very few early Americans used rugs on their floors. Instead, the floors were painted with colorful designs. Some homeowners covered their floors with tiny drops of paint. Other Americans painted canvas "carpets," to make the flooring look like costly rugs.

_____

2.   There is a strange little worm in South America called the railroad worm. This little animal looks as if it is divided into parts. A light is on each part. When we look at the worm at night, it looks like a number of lighted train windows.

_____

3.   It is said that a million matches can be made from one tree. It is also said that one match can destroy a million trees. This has happened. One careless person with one small match has destroyed in a very short time what nature has taken many years to make.

_____

4.   A woman in Pittsburgh can write or draw with both hands at the same time. Her name is Ellen Connor. With one hand she writes forward, in the ordinary way. With the other she writes backward. She can do this because of a special way her brain works.

_____

5.   In the 1920s, the average person lived to be only fifty-four years old. Since then, the length of a person's life has increased by about twenty years. More healthful foods and cleaner conditions in the world have helped make longer lives for humans possible.

1. Rugs for many early Americans were probably—

    (A) too costly
    (B) of little interest
    (C) used to hide fine wooden floors

---

2. The railroad worm must also look somewhat like—

    (A) a street light
    (B) an automobile
    (C) a lighted bus

---

3. You can tell that one—

    (A) match can do more good than one tree
    (B) tree can do more good than one match
    (C) match can do a great deal of harm

---

4. You can tell that—

    (A) Ms. Connor writes faster than other people
    (B) not everyone can learn to write like Ms. Connor
    (C) Ms. Connor needs a mirror to read

---

5. You can tell that the average person of the 1990s will—

    (A) die before reaching sixty
    (B) age faster than ever
    (C) live to be seventy-four

1.   A hotel in Japan has a gold bathtub. The hotel charges about five dollars to take a quick dip in the golden tub. Such a dip is supposed to add three years to one's life. People stand in long lines as they wait their turn.

---

2.   Fish can actually become seasick. They aren't seasick swimming in a river or ocean. Yet if live fish are shipped in cans, they do get sick if they have eaten. Fish shouldn't be given food for at least five days before they travel.

---

3.   In order to trap mustangs, Plains Indians of old waited at the waterhole. At night, when the mustangs came to drink, the Indians waited until the horses were full. Then they would chase after the water-filled mustangs on their own horses.

---

4.   During colonial days most people didn't use forks. People balanced food on the flat end of a knife. It was hard to pick up peas this way. Honey was smeared over the peas so they would cling to the knife.

---

5.   Skipping breakfast will not help a person lose weight. Eating three balanced meals a day can help shed pounds, though. Of these meals, breakfast is probably the most necessary of all. Milk, bread, fruit, and a source of protein should be included in the morning meal.

1. You can tell that many Japanese—

    (A) are very fussy about being clean

    (B) have no bathtubs at home

    (C) believe things can have magic powers

2. You can tell that fish travel best—

    (A) in small cans

    (B) on a full stomach

    (C) on an empty stomach

3. After they drank water, the mustangs—

    (A) ran faster

    (B) ran more slowly

    (C) wanted to sleep

4. The honey was used because it—

    (A) was sweet

    (B) tasted best with peas

    (C) was sticky

5. You can tell that—

    (A) snacks are necessary

    (B) breakfast is an important meal

    (C) a person can lose weight by skipping meals

1.   Scouts and animal lovers in Florida worked hard to capture turtles, called gopher tortoises, on an empty piece of land. Why? A new food factory would soon be built in this sandy, dry area in which the gopher tortoises burrowed. Many of the tortoises were saved and taken to parks and nature centers.

2.   When the wind stops blowing, sea waves do not stop moving. They get flatter and look like low hills. Once the waves are flattened out, they are called swells. Swells move across the ocean for hundreds of miles or even thousands of miles.

3.   Which type of animal can move the fastest—a land animal, a sea animal, or an air animal? The fastest fish can swim sixty miles an hour. The fastest mammal—the cheetah—runs at seventy miles per hour. The fastest bird—the duck hawk—can fly over 170 miles per hour.

4.   Most birds fly forward only—moving straight ahead, to the right or left, or up and down. Hummingbirds can fly backward and stay in one spot as well. Helicopters have been designed to fly like hummingbirds. The flying machines can go backward and hover, or pause in flight, the way hummingbirds do.

5.   Billions of tiny, shrimplike animals known as krill live in the ocean. Their hard outer shells seem to give them plenty of safety—but not when they're being swallowed by a 150-ton whale. Krill are the favorite food of baleen whales.

1. You can tell that—

   (A) gopher tortoises like to live in wet swamps
   (B) the tortoises that weren't rescued died
   (C) there are no longer any gopher tortoises in Florida

2. You will find swells—

   (A) when the wind is blowing
   (B) never travel far
   (C) on calm days

3. You can tell that—

   (A) no bird can catch the fastest fish
   (B) no mammal can catch the fastest fish
   (C) no mammal can catch the fastest bird

4. You can tell that designers of helicopters have—

   (A) nicknamed them *whirlybirds*
   (B) learned many bird calls
   (C) studied the way hummingbirds fly

5. You can tell that—

   (A) whales break open the shells of krill before eating
   (B) krill cannot protect themselves from whales
   (C) krill and whales are about the same size

A. Exercising Your Skill

The word *whale* is on each of the lists below. For each list, draw a **conclusion** about how a whale is like the other things on the list. On your paper, write a word or group of words as a heading for each list that tells how the things are alike. On the line under each list, write the name of one thing that could be added to the list.

1. _____   3. _____

   whale   whale

   seaweed   dolphin

   starfish   rabbit

   sea turtles   panda

   _____   _____

2. _____   4. _____

   whale   whale

   mountain   what

   elephant   which

   house   whisper

   _____   _____

B. Expanding Your Skill

Compare your headings and the words you added to the lists with your classmates' headings and words. Did you draw the same conclusions about each list? Discuss how the things in each list are alike. Then write other words that belong in each of the lists.

C. Exploring Language

The passages below give some facts about whales. For each passage, draw a conclusion from the facts that are given. Write the conclusion on your paper.

1. The blue whale is the largest animal on earth. It can grow to a length of more than 100 feet. Other large whales include humpback, right, and sperm whales. These whales can grow to a length of 60 feet. Some whales, though, are only $4\frac{1}{2}$ feet long.

2. At birth, a blue whale may be 25 feet long and weigh 2 tons. Each day, a baby blue whale grows about $1\frac{1}{2}$ inches longer and gains up to 200 pounds. When it is seven months old, it can weigh 25 tons!

3. Most animal babies are born head first. Whales and dolphins are born tail first. This keeps the babies from drowning during birth. Like all mammals, whales have lungs, not gills as fish do. Whales need air to breathe. Right after birth, the mother whale helps her baby, called a calf, come to the ocean's surface.

D. Expressing Yourself

Choose one of these activities.

1. Write a few sentences giving facts about a whale or other animal that you know something about. Then see whether a classmate can draw a conclusion about the animal.

2. Make up a list of things that go together like the lists in Part A. Ask your classmates to tell you how the things are alike. Have them name more things that could go on the list.

1.   A person who calls someone else a "silly goose" should think again. The goose is a very smart animal, not a silly one. Geese make marvelous "watchdogs." They will recognize certain persons as strangers and attack them fiercely.

2.   Shipworms make holes in wood. In a short time they can destroy boats that are made of wood. In one day just one shipworm can bore a hole three-quarters of an inch deep. The life of a boat isn't long when the shipworms go to work.

3.   When wine is made, the leftover waste includes a sour liquid. It is called *vinegar,* which means "sour wine" in French. French cooks discovered that adding vinegar makes salads, sauces, and other foods more delicious. Today, almost every kitchen shelf contains a bottle of vinegar.

4.   Plants often have names that fit them perfectly. The waxy white flowers of Indian pipes hang from white stems and are shaped like pipes. Cattails, which have many tiny brown flowers growing on long stalks, look like the tails of cats. Pussy willows have fuzzy gray buds that fluff out like little kittens.

5.   If you'd like to stay in a motel that's different, go to Strasburg, Pennsylvania, a small town near Lancaster. The motel, known as "The Red Caboose," is made up of thirty-seven railroad cars.

1. If you were a stranger at a farm, the goose would—

    (A) act silly for you
    (B) bark at you
    (C) attack you

    _____

2. The best way to stop shipworms is to—

    (A) find a fish that eats worms
    (B) buy a boat made of metal
    (C) replace all the boards having holes

    _____

3. Most people probably don't—

    (A) buy vinegar
    (B) like vinegar
    (C) drink vinegar

    _____

4. Plants have often been named for the—

    (A) color of their flowers
    (B) season of the year in which they bloom
    (C) way they look

    _____

5. The motel in Strasburg would be of special interest to—

    (A) campers
    (B) car owners
    (C) train lovers

1. Would you believe that any bird's nest could weigh over a ton? One bald eagle's nest at Vermillon, Ohio, measured twelve feet deep and weighed two tons! The bald eagle builds its aerie to last a lifetime, always repairing and adding to the original nest.

---

2. Some horses are said to become "loco," or insane, from eating locoweed. They stagger around half blind and chew on tin cans or old bones—anything at all, even barbed wire. Their joints get stiff. Their coats become rough. Soon death puts an end to their suffering.

---

3. Have you ever looked at the moon and seen a face, or perhaps an animal? Through the ages people have seen a man's face, a woman weaving, or a rabbit. What they really have been seeing, however, are features of the moon's surface—the mountains, valleys, and flat waterless "seas."

---

4. Roseburg, Oregon, used to have "weather goats." When the goats roamed high on a nearby mountain, people knew the weather would be good. When the goats grazed near the bottom, bad weather always followed. The people liked their weather goats so much they put up "goat crossing" road signs to protect them.

---

5. Put a pencil into a glass of water. Look at the pencil at the place where it enters the water. The pencil looks broken, doesn't it? This is because light doesn't travel as fast in water as it does in air. This causes the light rays to bend.

1. You can tell that—

   (A) all the eagles have left Ohio

   (B) an aerie is an eagle's nest

   (C) an eagle can move its nest easily

2. The weed got its name from—

   (A) its color

   (B) its location

   (C) what it causes

3. You can tell that—

   (A) the moon is completely level

   (B) the "Man in the Moon" is a real person

   (C) the moon looks different to different people

4. To reach the mountain, the goats must have to—

   (A) be carried in trucks

   (B) wade across a creek

   (C) cross a road

5. The pencil wouldn't seem to bend if light traveled in water at—

   (A) different speeds

   (B) the same speed

   (C) twice its speed

1. Long ago, pens were made from the feathers or quills of a goose or a wild turkey. The end of the quill was sharpened with a small knife. The knife that turned a quill into a pen was called a penknife. Today it is still called a penknife or a jackknife.

2. Lake Charles, Louisiana, may be the home of the world's largest birdhouse. It rises 120 feet into the air. There is room enough for over five thousand birds. The birdhouse was built in memory of the men and women who served our country in war.

3. People have loved gold since ancient times. Unlike harder metals, gold is not strong enough for making things like swords or cooking pots. Its beauty, though, makes it the perfect metal for decorative objects. Golden objects of great beauty are found all over the world.

4. Look at the wings of a bird in flight. Does the bird flap them together? Does it flap them at the same time? Does the bird flap first one and then the other? The chimney swift is the only bird that doesn't flap both wings together.

5. Different parts of the body have different temperatures. The average temperature for the body itself is 98.6 degrees. The skin is eight to ten degrees cooler. In cold weather hands and toes may be fifty degrees cooler. No wonder we need gloves and heavy socks in winter!

1. Another good name for the knife would be—

   (A) chicken knife

   (B) cut knife

   (C) quill knife

2. The people decided to honor the dead by—

   (A) helping the living

   (B) helping the dead

   (C) planting trees

3. You can tell that gold—

   (A) is difficult to work with

   (B) is one of the softer metals

   (C) was discovered recently

4. Most birds you see flap—

   (A) one wing, then the other

   (B) just one wing

   (C) both wings together

5. You can tell that—

   (A) the fingers are colder than the toes

   (B) the heart is warmer than the fingertips

   (C) the skin is about 108.6 degrees

1.   The town of Ochopee, Florida, has the smallest post office in the United States. It is only eight feet long and seven feet wide. It was once a tool shed. Only four people can fit inside at a time. Two of those people work there.

---

2.   Lake Superior is the largest of the five Great Lakes of North America. It covers more surface area than any other freshwater body in the world. However, Lake Baikal in Russia is about a mile deep. Because of this, it holds as much water as all five Great Lakes combined.

---

3.   Very young children often call a cat a "meow." They name the cat after the sound it makes. This is what people did in Egypt two thousand years ago. They called cats "mau," which sounds much like meow. Owners in China today still call the cat "meow."

---

4.   The word *corn* originally meant any kind of food grain. Corn might be wheat, rye, oats, or barley. When English settlers came to America, the American Indians showed them how to grow and use the grain that we call corn. In England, this grain from the New World was called *maize*.

---

5.   In the desert there are sometimes only three inches of rain a year. Thirty inches of rain a year helps farmers have very good crops. Sixty inches of rain is too much. It is likely to cause floods and damage to crops.

1. This post office can hold—

    (A) no customers at all

    (B) four customers at a time

    (C) two customers at a time

2. Lake Baikal—

    (A) is one of the five Great Lakes

    (B) is more beautiful than Lake Superior

    (C) has more water than any lake on Earth

3. The same kind of name for a dog would be—

    (A) Lassie

    (B) Rover

    (C) Bowwow

4. The grain that we call corn—

    (A) has always been popular in England

    (B) is really a kind of wheat

    (C) was brought to England from America

5. A year with ten inches of rain would bring—

    (A) poor crops

    (B) very healthy crops

    (C) flood-damaged crops

1. Our fingernails grow about three or four times as fast as our toenails. The fingernails that are on the longest fingers grow faster than the fingernails on the shorter fingers. The nails grow faster in the summer than in the winter.

_____

2. Long ago some people in Maine believed they knew how to cure a cold. They tied a dirty woolen sock around the neck. Sometimes they used a different "cure" for the cold. They tied the skin of a dead fish to their feet.

_____

3. If you watch a field of sunflowers on a sunny day, you will see a surprising sight. In the morning, the heads of the flowers are all facing toward the east. As the day continues, thousands of blossoms slowly turn so as to keep the sun shining directly on their heads.

_____

4. The lion has often been called "king of the jungle." This powerful hunter actually lives in open country—mostly in the grasslands of Africa. Male lions may look like kings with their beautiful manes, but female lions are usually the leaders of the group and do nearly all of the hunting.

_____

5. Many people have seen horses and dogs running at full speed. Yet they find it hard to believe that a horse is completely off the ground one of every four seconds. Dogs that are running at full speed are completely off the ground almost two of every four seconds.

1. Fingernails grow fastest on the—

   (A) first finger

   (B) middle finger

   (C) thumb

2. One cure was likely to—

   (A) work

   (B) cost a lot

   (C) cause dirty necks

3. You can tell that sunflowers—

   (A) are unusually beautiful plants

   (B) turn their heads to follow the sun

   (C) close their blossoms at night

4. This passage disagrees with the idea that lions—

   (A) hunt in groups

   (B) are jungle animals

   (C) are powerful beasts

5. When both run at full speed, dogs are off the ground—

   (A) less than horses

   (B) more than horses

   (C) the same amount as horses

1.   An alligator snapping turtle goes hunting by sitting still at the bottom of a river or lake. It opens its mouth wide and sticks out its tongue. The soft pink tip of its tongue wiggles like a worm. When a fish sees it, it swims near. Snap! The turtle's powerful jaws capture the fish.

2.   Before you climb a ladder, be sure to check it for safety. Make sure the feet have rubber or plastic "shoes" that will keep it from slipping. Check to see that there are no cracks, splits, or bent areas. Never lean a ladder against a window or a door.

3.   People are said to wake up head first. They are able to turn their heads to look at the alarm clock before they can actually reach out and turn off the alarm. The arms seem to wake up shortly afterward. The leg muscles are last to wake up.

4.   We may go to sleep to help our minds, not our bodies. A scientist says that the real reason we sleep is so that we can dream. Through dreams we often get our worries and fears out of our minds. When we awake feeling good, it may be because we have dreamed our troubles away.

5.   Fish can see people through the glass of a fishtank. They probably can't make out the features of a person, nor can they see far away. Yet fish seem to know owners who have had them for a long time by the motions of the owners' hands.

1. You can tell that—

    (A) the alligator snapping turtle eats worms

    (B) snapping turtles cannot swim well

    (C) the snapping turtle's tongue fools the fish

---

2. You can tell that ladders—

    (A) should not be used when fixing windows

    (B) should not get their feet wet

    (C) can be dangerous to use

---

3. The newly awakened shouldn't use their—

    (A) heads right away

    (B) arms until after they have walked around

    (C) legs before they use their arms

---

4. If we didn't dream, we might wake up feeling—

    (A) happy

    (B) worried

    (C) sore

---

5. You can tell that fish—

    (A) learn something very fast

    (B) can't learn anything

    (C) learn something slowly

1.   Although Jane Addams grew up in a small town, her life's goal was to help the poor people of the cities. In 1889, she bought a big house in Chicago called Hull House. She started many programs for the children and adults of her neighborhood. In the first year, fifty thousand people came to Hull House. By 1890, the number had doubled.

_____

2.   Many years ago, people liked to enter a jingle match. Land was roped off. Nine people were blindfolded. They tried to catch a tenth person. They were given one-half hour. The tenth person wasn't blindfolded but had to wear bells!

_____

3.   A tree gets taller by building upward. New growth forms on top of the old. A branch that grows out of the trunk at five feet above the ground will remain at five feet above the ground no matter how tall the tree grows.

_____

4.   What bird lays the largest eggs? Pound for pound, no bird can compete with the kiwi. A five-pound kiwi lays an egg weighing more than a pound. Even the ostrich, weighing 250 pounds, lays eggs that are only slightly larger.

_____

5.   Movies like *Jaws* may make people think that all sharks eat humans on sight. This is not so. The sixty-foot whale shark is the largest of all sharks. It has a seven-foot-wide jaw, but it eats nothing over four inches long and is harmless to humans.

1. You can tell that—

   (A) Hull House was a beautiful home

   (B) the programs at Hull House were popular

   (C) Jane Addams stayed in Chicago only a short time

___

2. They could best catch the tenth person by—

   (A) all grabbing hands

   (B) running fast

   (C) listening carefully

___

3. If you put a nail in a tree trunk, it would—

   (A) get higher each year

   (B) remain at the same height

   (C) kill the tree

___

4. A ten-pound kiwi would lay an egg weighing about—

   (A) one pound

   (B) ten pounds

   (C) two pounds

___

5. You can tell that—

   (A) whale sharks can't eat three-inch fish

   (B) no kind of shark ever eats humans

   (C) whale sharks were not the stars of *Jaws*

A. Exercising Your Skill

A good detective uses clues to draw a **conclusion** about a crime. A good reader uses clues to draw a conclusion about the events in a story. Try your skill at being a detective. Read each of the sets of clues below. Then on your paper, write what you think happened.

EVENT 1

upset trash can	trash on ground	angry person
large dog	small pawprints	cat eating

What do you think happened? _____

EVENT 2

heavy rain	strong wind	dripping, wet man
damp newspaper	umbrella in trash	crowded bus

What do you think happened? _____

EVENT 3

woman on ground	half-painted house	knocked-down ladder
barking dog	blue pawprints	paintbrush on grass
spilled blue paint	cat in tree	paint on hands

What do you think happened? _____

B. Expanding Your Skill

Compare the conclusions you drew about each event with your classmates' conclusions. Did everyone arrive at the same conclusions? Talk about the clues you used in each case. Tell how they led you to draw your conclusions.

C. Exploring Language

Choose items from the list below. Put some of them together to make a set of clues about an event. You may want to add other items of your own. On your paper, write a few sentences that tell the conclusion you drew about the event. Then read your list to your classmates. (Do *not* read your conclusion.) See if they can tell what happened.

cloudy sky	laughing crowd	mysterious house
fireworks	treeless hillside	leaky rowboat
stubborn mule	darkness	cries of "Wow!"
wet people	marching band	owl in tree
enormous kite	scary sounds	small child
fishing rod	windy day	huge fish
children running	balloons	flat tire

D. Expressing Yourself

Choose one of these activities.

1. Make up a list of clues about an event. Then trade lists with a classmate. Write a few sentences that draw a conclusion based on your classmate's list of clues.

2. Play "Twenty Questions" with your classmates. The leader thinks of an object. The others ask questions that can be answered only by *yes* or *no*. They put the clues together to guess what the item is.

3. Work together with a group of classmates. Act out a scene. (This can be one of the events based on the clues in Part C.) See whether your other classmates can draw a conclusion about what is happening.

1.   In 1848, gold was discovered in California. News of the find quickly spread. At the beginning of 1849, 26,000 people lived in California. By the end of that year, 115,000 people lived there. For most people, though, the search for gold resulted only in disappointment.

2.   Flying fish don't really fly. Neither do flying squirrels. They glide through the air. A flying fish can go as far as a quarter of a mile on one glide. It can travel at speeds up to thirty miles per hour. A flying squirrel glides, too, but it can only go downward.

3.   Louis St. Cyr was the strongest man in history. Once he pushed a railroad freight car up a hill. On another occasion he held ropes attached to four huge farm horses. The horses pulled and pulled, but they could not budge St. Cyr!

4.   Long ago it was good manners to make a lot of noise while eating. People were told to smack their lips loudly. The louder they smacked them, the more tasty the meal. This was a way of letting the cook know how much they liked the food.

5.   The glass catfish has a glassy body that a person can see through without any difficulty. It has a silvery color and grows to be about seven inches long. It places itself in one spot and waves its body, much like a flag blowing in the wind.

1. Most people who went to California in 1849—

   (A) soon became rich

   (B) traveled by boat

   (C) hoped to find gold

---

2. You can tell that—

   (A) fish can fly but squirrels cannot

   (B) flying fish travel quickly through air

   (C) flying fish glide only downward

---

3. Louis proved to be—

   (A) no match for four horses

   (B) stronger than a train

   (C) as strong as four farm horses

---

4. Dinnertime of long ago must have been—

   (A) noisy

   (B) quiet

   (C) pleasant

---

5. This fish looks—

   (A) as if it should be eaten

   (B) just like most other fish

   (C) much like a window

1.   In a new kind of rodeo, cowboys or cowgirls try to ride wild mules instead of horses. People who have seen a mule rodeo say the mules are much wilder than horses. Mule rodeos are exciting to watch. Mule-raisers send their wildest, meanest, most stubborn mules to the rodeos.

---

2.   You can use invisible ink to write secret messages. Just dip a toothpick in lemon juice or onion juice and use it to write your message on paper. Let the juice dry. Later your friend can make the message appear by holding the paper next to a hot lightbulb.

---

3.   Lantern fish are very unusual. They have organs or glands on the sides of the head and body, which give off light much like a lantern. Whether it swims deep in the ocean or up near the surface, the lantern fish lights its own way.

---

4.   Scientists believe that the owl can see shades of color that cannot be seen by humans. The heat waves coming from the tiny body of a mouse cannot be seen by the human eye. The owl sees these waves as red light. This ability enables the owl to hunt on the darkest nights.

---

5.   One plant of South Africa is often called the "window plant." Its pale green leaves are smooth. Only the tips of the leaves stick up from the dry ground in which it grows. You can see through the upper part of the leaves.

1. You can tell that—

   (A) there are no more horse rodeos

   (B) there were no mule rodeos in the old days

   (C) mule-raisers make it easy for the riders

2. You can tell that—

   (A) invisible ink is difficult to make

   (B) heat makes the message show up

   (C) most people write with lemon juice

3. The lantern fish lights up so that—

   (A) people can see it

   (B) it can see where it is going

   (C) its enemies will know it's coming

4. You can tell that—

   (A) owls have the best vision of all living things

   (B) humans have the best vision of all living things

   (C) vision differs among creatures

5. People can see—

   (A) the stem of the plant

   (B) little of the plant

   (C) all of the plant

1.   The camel has strong, yellow teeth. It is able to chew almost anything. It doesn't seem to care what it eats. Most camels will eat cactuses. Others have been known to eat bones and blankets. No matter what they eat, they don't seem to get sick.

---

2.   A reindeer's antlers make it difficult when the animal wants to look up. Large and heavy, the antlers are in the way when a reindeer wants to eat. Although the antlers fall off each year, within six months they are fully grown once again.

---

3.   Long ago, people feared mountains. They thought that dragons and giants lived in them. Some people believed that gods lived there. People of today don't look at mountains with fear. They look at them in the same way as they look at a pretty picture.

---

4.   Eugenie Clark is known as "the shark lady." She became interested in fish when she was a young child. Now she is one of the world's best-known scientists. She has spent many years studying sharks. Often she dives down deep in the ocean to swim with them underwater.

---

5.   The first modern electric-powered computer was built in the early 1940s by an American named Howard Aiken. It was fifty-one feet long and eight feet high and could do two addition problems per second.

1. You can tell that camels—

   (A) are very foolish

   (B) are like people

   (C) have strong stomachs

---

2. Reindeer have fully grown antlers for—

   (A) twelve months at a time

   (B) six months a year

   (C) two months a year

---

3. The people of long ago—

   (A) liked to live in the mountains

   (B) were very likely to ski down mountains

   (C) were not likely to visit mountains

---

4. Eugenie Clark—

   (A) is best known for her diving

   (B) prefers sharks to people

   (C) often works underwater

---

5. The first modern computer was—

   (A) smaller than today's computers

   (B) slower than today's computers

   (C) almost exactly like today's computers

1.   People don't get along well with poison ivy. Yet sheep, goats, pigs, and cattle eat it without any harm. People touch it and their skin itches, gets red, and blisters. Birds, bears, and other animals are lucky. Their skins are protected with feathers, fur, or hair.

2.   Lobsters move fastest when they are going backward. With a flip of its fan-shaped tail, the lobster shoots backward through the water. Its eyes are on stalks that move, so it can see in nearly any direction.

3.   In 1935 there were only two hundred trumpeter swans. Years before that they had ranged over much of the middle of our continent. Now these swans are no longer in danger. Their numbers are believed to be about five thousand in the United States.

4.   Do you know the old children's song "London Bridge"? The first London Bridge was built more than 700 years ago. It was a large bridge with little shops and houses all along it. Over the years, it did begin "falling down" many times, but it was always repaired. Finally it became too worn out to use. A new bridge now stands in its place.

5.   When winds blow across the ocean, they start waves. The stronger the wind, the higher the waves. Yet no matter how hard the wind blows and how high the waves reach, the water far below the surface is quiet and peaceful.

1. If people were covered with fur or feathers, they—

    (A) might not get poison ivy

    (B) would be bears or birds

    (C) would get poison ivy

2. You can tell that lobsters—

    (A) can see what is behind them

    (B) have flippers instead of legs

    (C) can move in only one direction

3. Long before 1935—

    (A) there were few swans

    (B) there were many swans

    (C) the swan wasn't known

4. You can tell that—

    (A) there are shops and houses on the new bridge

    (B) the song "London Bridge" is about the old bridge

    (C) the old bridge still stands near the new one

5. You can tell that waves—

    (A) are always very high

    (B) don't reach to the bottom

    (C) go all the way down

1.   Jean Baptiste du Sable was born in Haiti in 1745. He came to America when he was nineteen years old and traveled north to the shore of the Great Lakes, where he built a cabin and set up a trading post. Soon a settlement grew up around him. It became an important center for trade. Now it is one of the world's largest cities—Chicago, Illinois.

2.   The touch-me-not plant is not only pretty, but also rather interesting. It seems to glisten. One can almost see through its stem. Moreover, if one touches the plant, it explodes, sending its seeds flying out for quite a distance.

3.   People are said to go to sleep feet first. The leg muscles are the first muscles to become sleepy or drowsy. This spreads upward. Then the trunk and arm muscles get sleepy. The jaws and face are the last parts to become sleepy.

4.   There are about six quarts of blood in an adult's body. The six quarts pass through the heart in about two minutes when the body is resting. When the person is working very hard, all six quarts pass through the heart about three times in just one minute.

5.   When you throw a ball high in the air, why does it come right back down? A force you cannot see is pulling it down. The force is called *gravity*. Gravity pulls heavy things harder than lighter ones. The earth's gravity is six times stronger than the gravity on the moon.

UNIT 24

1. Jean Baptiste du Sable—

   (A) still lives in Chicago

   (B) built the first cabin in Chicago

   (C) was the founder of Haiti

   _____

2. You can see that the plant is—

   (A) found everywhere

   (B) like a mirror

   (C) most unusual

   _____

3. Muscles of the body—

   (A) never go to sleep

   (B) all go to sleep at the same time

   (C) go to sleep in a certain order

   _____

4. Blood moves faster when—

   (A) there is less blood

   (B) we work hard

   (C) we take things easy

   _____

5. You can tell that—

   (A) the earth is lighter than the moon

   (B) the moon has no gravity

   (C) you could throw a ball farther on the moon

1. The two basic types of elephants are African elephants and Asiatic elephants. Male African elephants measure about ten feet tall at the shoulder and weigh about 12,000 pounds. Asiatic males are about nine feet tall and weigh about 10,000 pounds. African elephants live up to sixty years, while Asiatic elephants may live as long as eighty.

---

2. In Boston during the early days, people did not work on Sundays. Sunday was set aside for worship only. It was against the law to run, cook, make a bed, sweep, or shave on Sundays. Some people even said it was wrong to be born on Sunday!

---

3. Acorns that fall from oak trees are a nuisance to people who like neat gardens. To others they are quite useful. In Europe, acorns are fed to pigs. In America, some people eat acorns from certain oaks. (Don't eat any without asking your parents.) Of course, acorns are a favorite meal of squirrels.

---

4. Sea otters are among the world's fastest swimmers. They dive deep in the water to gather clams for their food. When night comes, the sea otter wraps itself in seaweed near shore. The weeds make a soft nest and protect the otter from dangerous sharks.

---

5. There was a town in Florida built especially for horse-lovers. Every backyard had space for a stable as well as a garage. The planners of the town laid out almost thirty miles of horseback-riding trails. They also built a large area for horse shows. Even the streets had names like "Pony Drive."

1. African elephants—

   (A) are taller than Asiatic elephants

   (B) live longer than Asiatic elephants

   (C) are lighter than Asiatic elephants

2. In the early days, much of Sunday was spent in—

   (A) action

   (B) prayer

   (C) cleaning

3. You can tell that—

   (A) some acorns might harm you

   (B) only Europe and America have oaks

   (C) only Europe and America have squirrels

4. You can tell that—

   (A) sea otters hunt for food on the shore

   (B) seaweed is important to the sea otter's diet

   (C) sharks sometimes attack sea otters

5. This town would *not* have a street called—

   (A) "Horsehead Road"

   (B) "Saddle Avenue"

   (C) "Steamboat Street"

A. Exercising Your Skill

An analogy is a way of comparing things. An analogy shows how things that don't seem to be alike *are* alike in some way. It shows how two sets of things are alike. Read this analogy:

Cheap is to **expensive** as **first** is to **last**.

Cheap and *expensive* are opposites, and so are *first* and *last*. This analogy shows that this is the way these two sets of words are alike.

Analogies may be made about many different kinds of things. They may be about words with opposite meanings (antonyms), or words with similar meanings (synonyms). Analogies may also be about parts of whole things, and things and the groups they belong to.

Read each analogy below. Draw a conclusion about each set of things. Ask yourself whether the analogy makes sense. Then, on your paper, write *sense* or *no sense*.

1. **Oak** is to **tree** as **grass** is to **flower**.
2. **Knife** is to **sharp** as **stone** is to **hard**.
3. **Wolf** is to **howl** as **cat** is to **purr**.
4. **Paintbrush** is to **paint** as **hairbrush** is to **teeth**.
5. **Person** is to **house** as **bird** is to **den**.
6. **Mitten** is to **hand** as **scarf** is to **neck**.
7. **Day** is to **week** as **month** is to **year**.
8. **Angry** is to **mad** as **delighted** is to **happy**.
9. **Baker** is to **bread** as **barn** is to **garden**.
10. **Words** are to **dictionary** as **dreams** are to **encyclopedia**.

B. Expanding Your Skill

Discuss the analogies with your classmates. For each analogy that made sense, explain how the two sets of things are alike. For each analogy that did not make sense, tell why it did not. Then rewrite those analogies so that they do make sense.

C. Exploring Language

When you are asked to fill in a missing word in an analogy, you have to draw a conclusion. First, look at the words in the complete set and figure out how the words go together. Then write a word in the blank that completes the analogy.

1. **Honey** is to **sweet** as **lemon** is to _____ .
2. **Smoke** is to **chimney** as _____ is to **faucet**.
3. **Rough** is to _____ as **arrive** is to **leave**.
4. _____ is to **carpenter** as **wrench** is to **plumber**.
5. **Horse** is to **animal** as _____ is to **bird**.
6. A **run** is to _____ as a **touchdown** is to **football**.
7. **Chalk** is to **blackboard** as **pen** is to _____ .
8. **Nose** is to _____ as **toe** is to **foot**.
9. **Dark** is to **light** as _____ is to **bottom**.
10. **Baby** is to **person** as **puppy** is to _____ .

D. Expressing Yourself

Choose one of these activities.

1. Choose three categories from the list below. Make up an analogy for each category you choose.

   • synonyms
   • antonyms
   • parts of whole things
   • things that belong to groups
   • workers and their jobs or tools
   • things or people and their actions
   • animals and their young
   • things and their shape, color, sound, or taste

2. Think of an analogy. Then get four index cards. Write part of the analogy on each card. Ask your classmates to put the cards in the right order and explain why the words go together.